comix

AGENT SPIKE AND THE VEGETABLES OF DOOM

Mark Burgess

Illustrated by Bridget MacKeith

D1615183

A & C Black • London

CAVAN COUNTY LIBRARY
ACC No. C/166686
CLASS NO. J/5-8
INVOICE NO 6022 IES
PRICE €6.72

comix

Published 2003 by A & C Black Publishers Ltd
37 Soho Square, London W1D 3QZ
www.acblack.com

Text copyright © 2003 Mark Burgess
Illustrations copyright © 2003 Bridget MacKeith

The rights of Mark Burgess and Bridget MacKeith to be identified as author and illustrator of this work have been asserted by them in accordance with the Copyrights, Designs and Patents Act 1988.

ISBN 0-7136-6574-2

A CIP catalogue record for this book is available from the British Library.

All rights reserved. No part of this publication may be reproduced in any form or by any means - graphic, electronic or mechanical, including photocopying, recording, taping or information storage and retrieval systems - without the prior permission in writing of the publishers.

A & C Black uses paper produced with elemental, chlorine-free pulp, harvested from managed sustainable forests.

Printed and bound in Spain by G. Z. Printek, Bilbao

CHAPTER ONE

Spike was hard at work at school. Suddenly, the screen in front of him flickered. His Aunt Emily appeared. She was director of the Secret Service. This could mean only one thing – an urgent job for Agent Spike.

CAVAN COUNTY LIBRARY

Don't you mean hostages, Auntie?
Yes, that's right, sausages.
Anyway, the prime minister is due to visit this afternoon. So we must stop a leek reaching the press.
I'll get on to it!

Thank you, Spike. I'll let Lucy know you're on your way. I knew I could rely on you. You're the best person for the job. You're so good with vegetables. Look at the way you help your mum in the garden!
It was true. Spike was brilliant at growing vegetables.
I'm on my way, Auntie.

Quickly, Spike set up a hologram so that his teacher wouldn't notice that he'd gone.

Then he sneaked out of the classroom. He ran to get his scooter.

Instantly, Spike's scooter morphed into a speed pod.

A few minutes later, Spike approached the research station. The gates appeared to be guarded. He swerved off the road before he was spotted.

CHAPTER TWO

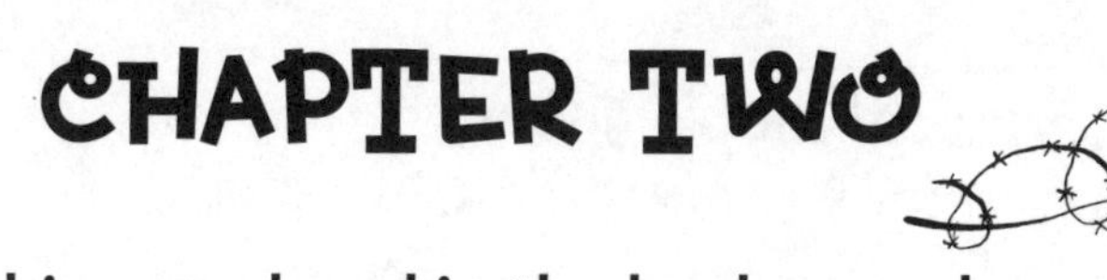

Spike hid his speed pod in the bushes and crept closer. There were guards everywhere.

Spike crawled nearer, keeping out of sight.

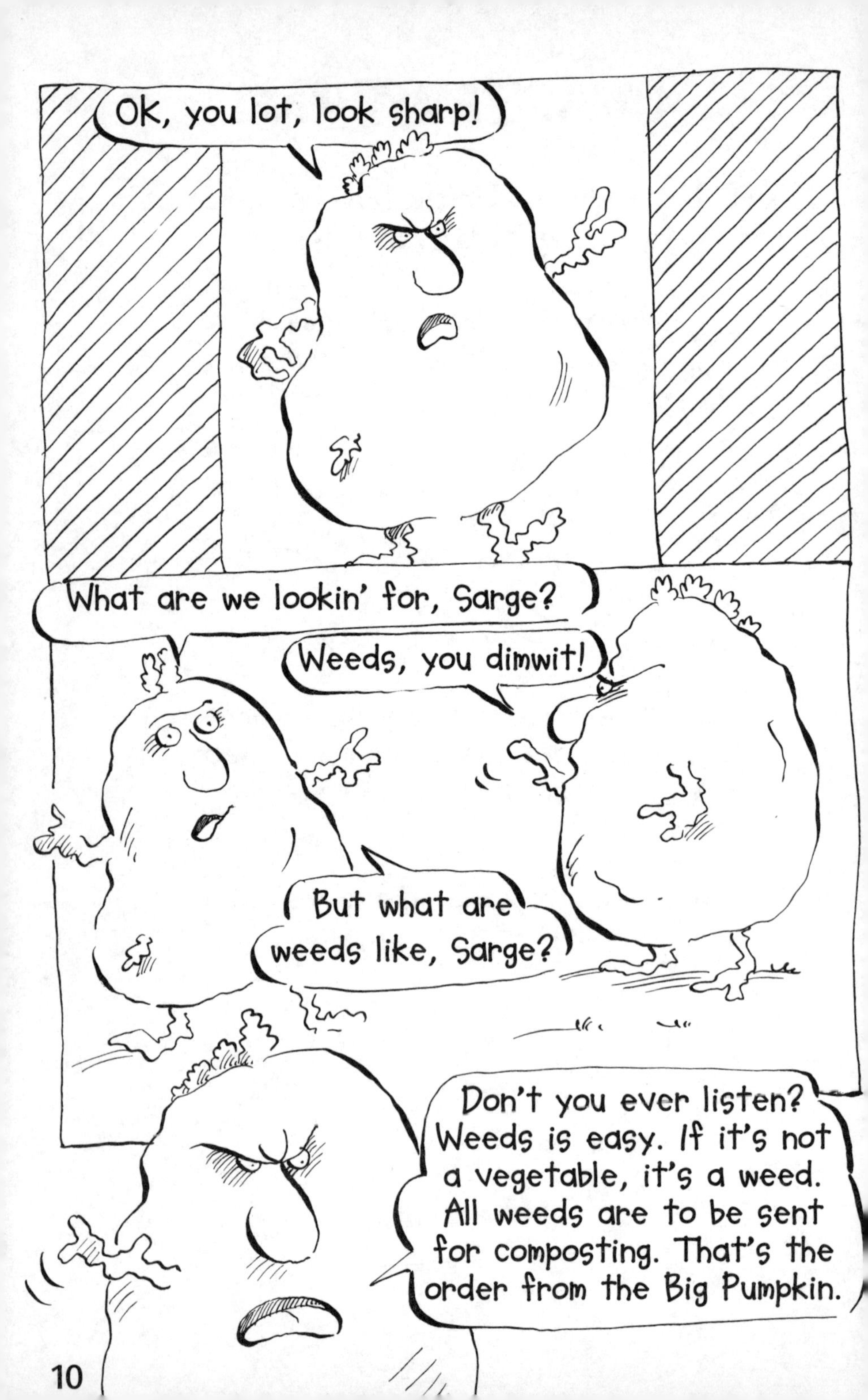
OK, you lot, look sharp!
What are we lookin' for, Sarge?
Weeds, you dimwit!
But what are weeds like, Sarge?
Don't you ever listen? Weeds is easy. If it's not a vegetable, it's a weed. All weeds are to be sent for composting. That's the order from the Big Pumpkin.

nod nod
What about a flower, Sarge, is that a weed?
s-c-r-a-t
Is a flower a vegetable? Of course not. So it's a weed, isn't it? Now don't ask any more stupid questions!
A cloud isn't a vegetable ... So is a cloud a weed, Sarge?
Aarrgghhh!!!

So it's total domination they're planning? That's awful! We need different plants and animals in the world. I must put a stop to this. But I'd better look out – I don't fancy being composted.
Spike crept away, keeping under cover of the bushes.
I'll find a bit of the fence that isn't guarded. Then I'll climb over, and contact Lucy when I'm safely inside.

Spike followed the fence around the institute buildings. He came to a part where there were no guards.
This'll do. Here goes.
Spike leapt the fence. But suddenly, runner beans sprang from nowhere.

They scrambled after Spike ...
Help, I've been spotted!
I MUST reach that building.
Running as fast as he could, he just made it and began to climb.
But tough tendrils curled around Spike's ankles, pulling him back.

Ah, ha! We've been stalking you, we have. And you didn't notice! Tee-hee, weedy-weed! Now we've got you!
Help! Let go!
Weed! Weed! Compost feed!
Spike struggled hard but the tendrils got tighter and tighter. He was losing his grip.
I'm not a weed! Let go!
Ha, ha! It's off to the compost bin for you!

CHAPTER THREE

The runner beans were tugging hard. Spike was desperate. Then he had an idea.

In an instant, Spike was up the side of the building. He was in through a ventilation hatch before the beans had realised what was happening.

Spike switched on his wrist communicator.

Agent Lucy appeared on the screen. She looked as if she were in trouble. Strange red blobs were swarming all over her.

Spike was worried. Perhaps Agent Lucy was being softened up, ready for composting. He must get to her quickly.
As Spike crawled along the ventilation shaft, he checked his wrist communicator.
The tracking light is getting stronger. Not far now.
Spike peeped through a hatch. There were two red peppers on the other side of the grille. They were guarding a door.

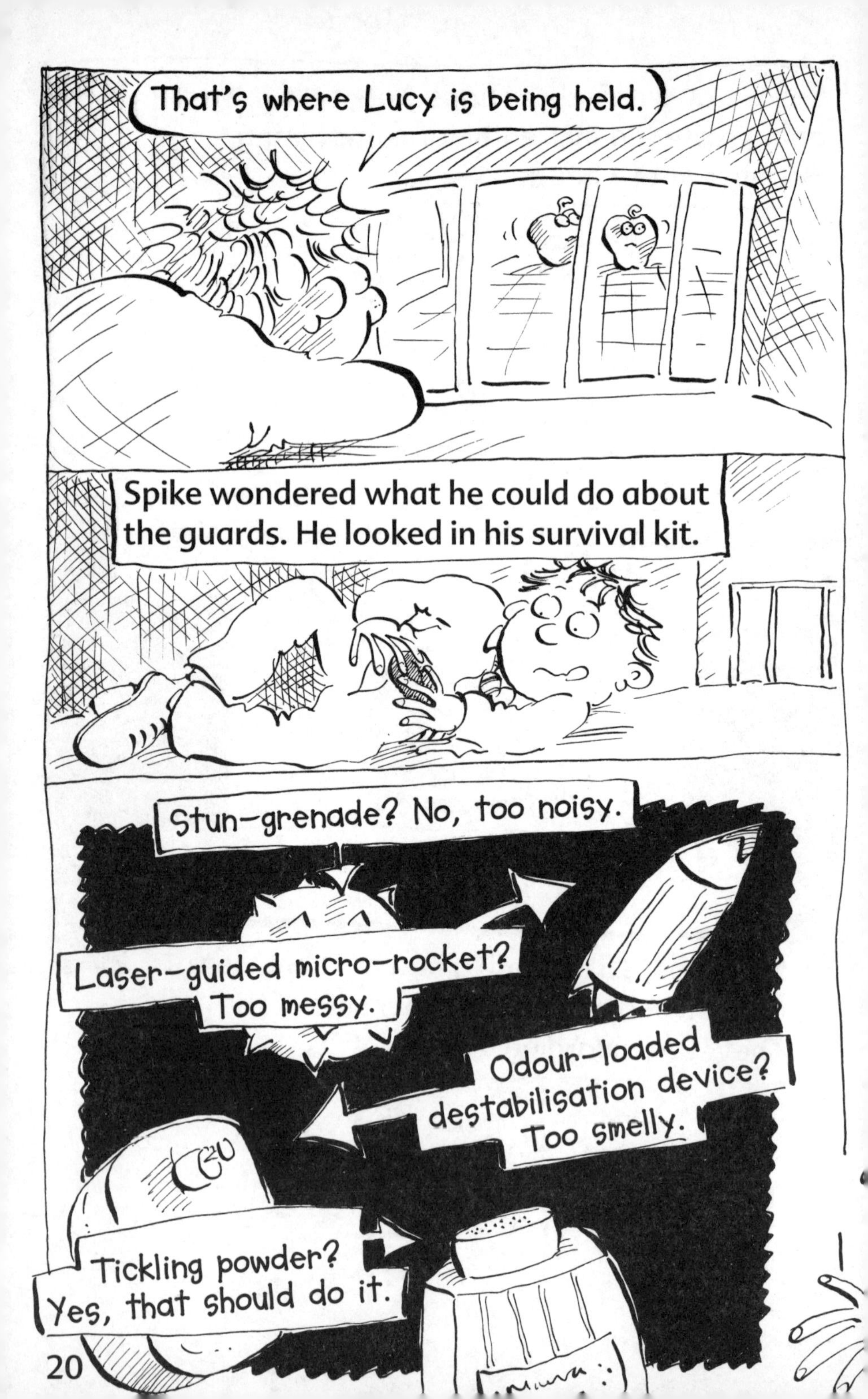
That's where Lucy is being held.
Spike wondered what he could do about the guards. He looked in his survival kit.
Stun-grenade? No, too noisy.
Laser-guided micro-rocket? Too messy.
Odour-loaded destabilisation device? Too smelly.
Tickling powder? Yes, that should do it.

Spike leapt out of the ventilation shaft and flung the tickling powder at the peppers. They fell to the ground, giggling uncontrollably.
Hee-hee-hee-hee! Oh, ha-ha-ha-ha! Oh, Stop! Stop! I can't stand it! Hee-hee-hee-hee!
Spike dashed past them and through the door.
Lucy! Are you all right?
Before she could answer, Spike stopped dead in his tracks.

CHAPTER FOUR

Tummmaddddos! I mean tomatoes! What the—?
It's perfectly understandable. They are just going through their standard appraisal and welcoming routine. The computer simulation predicted such a result. All most gratifying.

Spike, this is Professor Finkbottle. Professor, this is Agent Spike.
Hellumppff, profffudddor.
How d'you do, Spike? Welcome to Dundiggin. As I was saying, all the data indicates that this behaviour is a direct result of the environmentally friendly culture techniques employed in this experiment.
The tomatoes have all become very friendly.
I can see that!

Project T was very successful. In fact, rather more so than we expected. Unfortunately, the other vegetables ...
Let's not talk about it now, Professor. We've got to sort out this mess before the prime minister arrives this afternoon. What's the latest, Lucy?

The vegetables are being led by the Big Pumpkin. I found that out before I had to run for it with the Professor. There are regular patrols throughout the institute and all weeds are being sent to the compost bin.
I nearly got a taste of that. Anything that isn't a vegetable is treated as a weed!
We hid in here and the Project T tomatoes saved us. They refused to join the Big Pumpkin. But a guard was put outside so we were stuck until you arrived.

I put the guards out of action to get past but they'll have recovered by now. Is there another way through the building? We might be able to take them by surprise and gain control.
?
All the laboratories in this section are linked by just one corridor. It was thought sensible in case we needed to isolate a room in the event of a major incident.

So that's that. We're stuck.
There is the service tunnel, of course ...
What? Underground? How do we get in to it?
Over here.

CHAPTER FIVE
They ran to the spot where Professor Finkbottle was standing. Quickly, Spike lifted the hatch.
What about the tomatoes?
Can they stay here? This could be dangerous.
I'll talk to them and reassure them.

The tomatoes gathered round the Professor.
Yes, yes, I'll be careful. You'll be safe here. We won't be long.
KWUPPT!
KWUPPT!
KWUPPT!

Spike climbed down the ladder, into the tunnel.
Then the Professor and Lucy followed.
Drat! My torch isn't working. It must have been damaged when I leapt over the perimeter fence.
Mine's OK. Let's go!
The vegetables will be up in the central control room. There were some already there when I passed on the way in.
That's this way.

Spike switched on his torch and they began to scramble along the tunnel. It was cramped, with cables and pipes everywhere.

The Professor bumped his head.

What? Yes, I think so ... That was the main water supply pipe. Did you know we use 435 gallons daily? And that's just the water. The daylight simulation illuminators use over 300 kilowatts of—
THUNK
Spike! The Professor - I think he's unconscious!

Spike rushed back to where the Professor had fallen.
Professor, speak to me!

Eh? I was, wasn't I? Oh, did I fall over? Thank you. Where was I? Yes, now that's the main electricity cable. It supplies the whole complex with ...

They reached a junction in the tunnel.
Shh! – something's moving overhead. Which way now, Professor?
Let me see. This way. No, that way. Yes, that's the way.

Drat, now my torch is giving out!
T-H-U-M-P
TH-U-M-P
Surely it's not much further? We can feel our way.
T-H-U-N-K
Ow!
Spike! Are you OK?

Suddenly, there was a scuffle in the tunnel.

CHAPTER SIX

First Division Carrot Patrol, apprehend prisoners!
Carrots!
You are surrounded. Resistance is pointless.

Project C! The high levels of carotene mean they can see in absolute darkness.
n-o-d n-o-d
Very impressive.
You took the wrong route ...
But we rooted you out! First Division Carrots are the best!
OK, you two, take them to our Weeder.

The carrots marched Spike, Lucy and the Professor along the tunnel.
Up these steps! Get a move on, we haven't got all day.
Hey! Stop pushing!
They emerged in the central control room. It was full of vegetables. They were cheering the Big Pumpkin.
Hooray!

The Big Pumpkin signalled for silence.
Fellow vegetables! I promise you that soon our environment will be weed-free. All vegetables will live in peace and harmony. But remember, fellow vegetables – for a better, weedless world, we must always be vigilant! Be vigilant vegetables!
Hooray! Hooray!

The carrots pushed their prisoners to the front.
Ah, I see we have some visitors. Step forward.
Weeds! Weeds!
I am NOT a weed!

Be careful, Professor.
Then are you a vegetable?
No! Of course I'm not a vegetable! Do I look like a vegetable? Do you think a vegetable could run this institute? What an idea! A vegetable running the institute! Ha!

Enough of this babble! So, you're not a vegetable? Then you're a weed! Anything that isn't a vegetable is a weed!

Weed! Weed!

At once, the vegetables began to push Spike, Agent Lucy and the Professor towards the door.

CHAPTER SEVEN

Spike was thinking fast. How could he get them out of this mess? Then, suddenly, he had an idea ...

Yes, we are! We're the best – HUMAN BEANS!
Nonsense. I've never heard of them.
I can prove it. I'll show you the pod I arrived in!
The Big Pumpkin paused. All vegetables knew that beans came in pods.

The Big Pumpkin sent a couple of cucumbers to find the pod. Everybody went outside to wait.

It wasn't long before the cucumbers returned.
Ooooooo!
The Big Pumpkin went to have a closer look.
What are these switches for?
They're the speed controls.

Really? Is it very fast?
Faster than ...
n-o-d
... a runner bean?
Nothing is faster
than a runner bean!
Nothing!
It's impossible!

The Big Pumpkin got on to the speed pod and pressed the controls.

Off went the Big Pumpkin, as fast as a rocket, narrowly missing a wall.

V-W-O-O-S-H!!!!!!

After a sharp turn, the Big Pumpkin nearly fell out. Back came the speed pod, straight towards the other vegetables.

Look out!

RUN FOR IT!

Everybody dashed out of the way, but only just in time. The Big Pumpkin sped by ...
Wheeeeeeeee!

Look at me!
... heading for the compost bin.
Spike shouted an instruction.
Pod: LOOP!
CONFIRMED!

Immediately, the pod did a loop-the-loop. Taken by surprise, the Big Pumpkin lost control and fell out ...
Eh?!

... straight smack into the compost bin.
SPLAT...
HI
LO

CHAPTER EIGHT

The vegetables were horrified that the Big Pumpkin had come to a sticky end. They ran around madly, completely lost without their leader.

Then, suddenly, the Professor appeared, followed by the Project T tomatoes. The tomatoes ran to comfort the other vegetables. They hugged and kissed them.
KUMPPT!!
There, there, it's all right! Don't worry!
KUMPPT!
KUMPPT!!

Gradually, the vegetables calmed down.
I never wanted to be tough. It's really against my nature.
That's me all over. I'm the tender sort.
KUMPPT
Me too! I only acted tough. Deep down, I'm soft-hearted.

Hello, Auntie. Mission accomplished.
Everything's under control.
Well done! That's how
I like my vegetables!
Spike hurriedly switched
off his wrist communicator.

I'd better be going, Professor. Keep up the good work!
The Professor, who was comforting the potatoes, waved goodbye.
Is your speed pod all right, Spike? I could give you a lift.
Thanks, Lucy, but it should be OK. This model is designed to withstand quite a smash.

Spike spoke to the speed pod.
Pod: ISSUE DAMAGE REPORT.
CONFIRMED.
The pod turned itself the right way up. Lights flashed on the control panel.
DAMAGE REPORT: NEGATIVE.
Good. Now I'd better get back to school.

CAVAN COUNTY
LIBRARY